CW00545623

THE D-DAY LANDINGS
THE COMIC STRIP

I. BOURNIER – S. CORBET

Isabelle Bournier

Isabelle Bournier is a historian and author of several documentaries for young readers. She is also cultural and educational manager at the Mémorial de Caen.

Sébastien Corbet

Sébastien Corbet is an illustrator. He was born in Caen in 1972. After studying in an advertising school, he turned his career towards music. Concurrently, he paints and, after exhibiting for ten years, resumed his earlier passion for comic strip.

Zone tertiaire de Nonant - 14400 BAYEUX
Tel: 02 31 51 81 31 - Fax: 02 31 51 81 32
info@orepeditions.com - www.orepeditions.com

Editor: Grégory Pique - Editorial coordinator: Sophie Lajoye
Layout: Laurent Sand - Graphic design: OREP Editions - English translation: Heather Inglis
ISBN: 978-2-8151-0472-2 - - Legal deposit: 2nd quarter 2019
Imprimé en France par Imprimerie de Champagne Langres 52.

French law n°49-956 dated 16th July 1949 on publications for young readers, modified by the law n°2011-525 dated 17th May 2011 – April 2019

We are in 1944. France is occupied by the German army. Over the night of the 5th to the 6th of June, thousands of boats, laden with troops and material, set sail from England. Their aim? To land on the Normandy beaches. France's liberation has just begun!

The Allies decide to land in Normandy

DECEMBER 1943, IN LONDON, GENERAL DWIGHT EISENHOWER HAS JUST BEEN NAMED COMMANDER-IN-CHIEF OF THE ALLIED FORCES. HIS MISSION IS TO PREPARE THE NORMANDY LANDINGS!

THE DECISION IS MADE! WE WILL LAND HERE!
BUT THERE'S NO PORT!?

EISENHOWER HAS GATHERED TOGETHER ALL THE ARMY AND AIR FORCE GENERALS AND THE NAVY ADMIRALS.

WE'RE GOING TO LAND ON THE BEACHES AND TAKE THE GERMANS BY SURPRISE.

THE OPERATION IS GIVEN THE CODENAME 'OVERLORD'.

THE LANDINGS WILL TAKE PLACE SIX MONTHS FROM NOW, EARLY JUNE. AND THEY WILL MARK THE BEGINNING OF EUROPE'S LIBERATION.

FOR MONTHS, THE ALLIED PLANES HAVE BEEN FLYING OVER AND OBSERVING THE ATLANTIC WALL.

OUR RECONNAISSANCE PATROLS HAVE BROUGHT BACK PHOTOGRAPHS.

LOOK AT THAT! THEY'VE INSTALLED GUNS EVERYWHERE!

NO, WAIT! THEIR DEFENCE IS MAINLY IN PORTS... THAT'S WHERE THEY'RE EXPECTING US.

THREE MONTHS LATER, IN THE SOUTH OF ENGLAND...

I'M FROM QUEBEC, AND YOU?
ME TOO, NEAR LAC SAINT-JEAN... IT'S A LONG WAY OFF...

THE SOLDIERS HAVE LEFT THE UNITED STATES AND CANADA, CROSSED THE ATLANTIC AND SET UP CAMP IN GREAT BRITAIN.

SOME GUYS ARE FROM THE STATES...
... AND EVEN AUSTRALIA ...

... OUR MISSION MUST BE KEPT SECRET... NOT A WORD... TO ANYONE!
WHAT WOULD WE SAY? WE DON'T EVEN KNOW WHERE WE'RE GOING TO LAND

DO YOU THINK THERE ARE GERMAN SPIES HERE?
IMPOSSIBLE! THEY WOULD'VE BEEN SPOTTED A LONG TIME AGO!

BUT SPIES THERE WERE... AND EVEN DOUBLE AGENTS... WHO GAVE INFORMATION BOTH TO THE GERMANS AND THE ALLIES.

GARBO, ARE YOU SURE THE GERMAN INTELLIGENCE HAS FAITH IN YOU?
service secrets

THE GERMANS NEVER FOUND OUT THAT GARBO WAS, IN FACT, A DOUBLE AGENT.

TOTAL FAITH! AND, WHAT'S MORE... AT LEAST THEY PAY ME WELL FOR IT.

Hitler has the Atlantic Wall built

IN 1942, HITLER DECIDES TO BUILD A CONCRETE WALL TO PROTECT THE EUROPEAN COAST FROM AN ALLIED LANDING OPERATION.

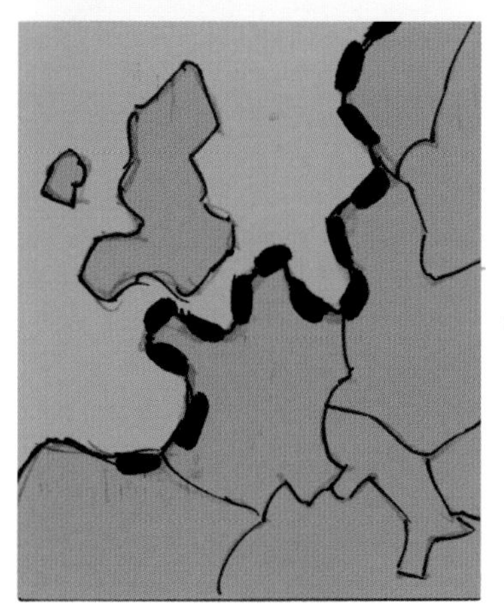

I WANT A WALL AND GUNS! FROM NORWAY TO THE SPANISH BORDER!
BUT!? *MEIN FÜHRER*, THAT WOULD MEAN A 4,000 KILOMETRE-LONG WALL!

FRENCH COMPANIES ARE REQUISITIONED TO BUILD THE ATLANTIC WALL. THEIR WORKERS ARE EITHER VOLUNTEERS OR FORCED LABOURERS.

WE NEED TO SPEED UP WORK!
BUT, I DIDN'T ASK TO COME HERE!

CAREFUL! THAT'S THE THIRD BAG YOU'VE DROPPED...
I'M SLOWING DOWN WORK AS BEST I CAN... WHAT ARE YOU WAITING FOR TO DO THE SAME?!
POUF!

BUT DO YOU KNOW THE RISKS!? ARE YOU NOT AFRAID?

BE CAREFUL! YOU SHOULDN'T BELIEVE EVERYTHING YOU READ IN THE NEWSPAPERS...

HITLER BUILDS AND IMPASSIBLE CONCRETE WALL!

CONTRARY TO WHAT THE GERMAN PROPAGANDA* HAS TO SAY, THE ATLANTIC WALL IS NOTHING LIKE A SOLID WALL AND, IN JUNE 1944, IT IS FAR FROM COMPLETE.

THIS WALL IS FULL OF HOLES! AND IT'S NOT GOING TO STOP THE ALLIES!

APRIL 1944: GENERAL ROMMEL** COMES TO INSPECT WORK. AND HE'S OBVIOUSLY NOT SATISFIED WITH WHAT HE CAN SEE!

IF YOU THINK THEY'RE GOING TO COME ON A SUNNY DAY, VIA THE SHORTEST ROUTE...
... AND THAT THEY'LL TELL US WHEN, THEN YOU'RE MISTAKEN.

GENERAL ROMMEL HAS HIS OWN IDEA ABOUT THE LANDINGS...

THE ALLIES WILL LAND IN APPALLING WEATHER... AND THEY WILL LAND HERE, IN NORMANDY...

...AND IT WILL BE THE LONGEST DAY.

LAND ON A BEACH! THERE'S NO RISK OF THAT HAPPENING... THOSE ALLIES ARE NOT CRAZY!

BACK AT EISENHOWER'S HEADQUARTERS IN LONDON...
ROMMEL HAS ORDERED FOR OBSTACLES AND MINEFIELDS TO BE INSTALLED ON THE BEACHES. THAT GENERAL IS CUNNING...

* INFORMATION SPREAD TO MAKE PEOPLE BELIEVE THAT THE WALL IS IMPASSIBLE.

** ERWIN ROMMEL (1891-1944): GENERAL IN COMMAND OF THE GERMAN ARMIES IN NORMANDY.

Soldiers in training

SOLDIERS TRAIN OVER SEVERAL WEEKS. PARACHUTE JUMPS, LANDING EXERCISES, FIRING WITH REAL BULLETS...

AT THE SIGNAL, JUMP!

IT'S ALL TANGLED UP!
YOU'RE NOT EXACTLY BRIGHT. DO YOU PREFER TANKS?

NOTHING IS LEFT TO CHANCE – NOT A DETAIL. THE ALLIES TRY TO ANTICIPATE ANYTHING THAT MIGHT HAPPEN IN NORMANDY.

HERE ARE THE MARSHES, WHERE YOU'RE MOST LIKELY TO DROWN...

... AND THERE, THE ENEMY, WHO'LL BE HAPPY TO FIRE AT YOU. YOU SHOULD AVOID BOTH!

WHAT IF WE GET LOST IN THE NIGHT?

CLICK! CLACK!... YOU'LL HAVE THIS. IT MIGHT EVEN SAVE YOUR LIFE.
CLIC
CLAC

JUMPING BETWEEN THE MARSHES AND THE GERMAN BULLETS WAS FAR FROM REASSURING FOR THE PARACHUTISTS...

THE SOUTH OF ENGLAND HAS BECOME A HUGE STORAGE ZONE FOR MILITARY MATERIAL. IT IS EVERYWHERE: IN THE FIELDS, ON THE ROADSIDE, IN FAMILY GARDENS AND COURTYARDS...

WE'LL NEVER GET THERE AT THIS SPEED!

LOOK AT THAT! ENGLAND HAS BECOME A HUGE CAR PARK!

2,578 ... 2,579 ... 2,580 JERRICANS! AND AS MANY TYRES IN THE NEXT FIELD.

SOLDIERS ARE CHATTING IN A MILITARY CAMP. THEY STILL HAVEN'T BEEN TOLD WHERE THEY ARE GOING. THE INFORMATION IS 'TOP SECRET'!

WHERE DO YOU THINK WE'RE GOING TO LAND?
BELGIUM, I RECKON.

SOME SAY WE'RE GOING TO NORTHEAST FRANCE. THAT'S WHERE THE COAST IS CLOSEST TO ENGLAND... IT'S LOGICAL.

AS THEY WAIT TO FIND OUT WHERE THEY ARE GOING, THE ALLIED SOLDIERS CONTINUE THEIR TRAINING.

TATATATATATATA
TATATA
HEY! CAREFUL! THEY'RE REAL BULLETS YOU KNOW!

IF YOU DON'T JUMP OUT OF YOUR BARGES FASTER THAN THAT ON D-DAY, YOU'LL ALREADY BE DEAD!

The British 'phantom' army

'FORTITUDE' IS A HUGE DIVERSION OPERATION SET UP BY THE ALLIES TO LEAD THE GERMANS TO BELIEVE THAT THE LANDINGS WILL BE IN THE NORTHEAST OF FRANCE.

PUMP HARDER!
I'M EXHAUSTED!

INFLATABLE TANKS, FAKE TRUCKS MADE OF WOOD, FAKE TRAINING EXERCISES... A PHANTOM ARMY AIMED AT DECEIVING THE ENEMY IS GATHERED TOGETHER IN SOUTHEAST ENGLAND.

CLEAR THE WAY!!

EVERYTHING IS FAKE... EXCEPT ITS COMMANDER: THE FAMOUS GENERAL PATTON!

AT EISENHOWER'S HEADQUARTERS...
IT ALL DEPENDS ON OPERATION 'FORTITUDE'. IF IT WORKS, WE'LL HAVE CONVINCED HITLER WE'RE GOING TO LAND IN PAS-DE-CALAIS...

... AND HE WON'T SEND REINFORCEMENTS TO NORMANDY. IT'S DOUBLE OR QUITS!

THE FAKE SHIP CONVOYS ARE IN PLACE SIR.
THE FAKE PARACHUTE DROPS TOO.

BACK IN BERLIN, HITLER HAS NO IDEA...
THE LANDINGS ARE IMMINENT AND...

... THEY'RE GOING TO LAND IN THE NORTHEAST OF FRANCE. AND THEN! HA! HA! OUR GUNS ARE GOING TO SMASH THEM TO PIECES!

The soldiers board. Their destination? Normandy!

1ST JUNE 1944, BACK IN ENGLAND, THE TIME HAS COME TO BOARD.

THE TROOPS WHO HAVE ALREADY BOARDED WAIT TO LEAVE. AND IT'S A LONG WAIT...

WE'VE BEEN WAITING FOR TWO DAYS NOW, ARE WE LEAVING OR NOT?

THEY'RE WAITING FOR THE WEATHER TO IMPROVE. APPARENTLY THERE'S A HUGE STORM OUT AT SEA.

GENERALS MONTGOMERY AND EISENHOWER DO NOT QUITE AGREE... SHOULD WE LAUNCH THE OPERATION? OR WAIT?

BUT WHAT ARE WE WAITING FOR?
BETTER WEATHER... WE MUST TAKE NO RISK WHATSOEVER.

THE WEATHER OFFICER BRINGS THE LATEST FORECAST. IT'S 4.30 IN THE MORNING.

AT LAST! A CALM SPELL IS COMING!

AFTER BEING POSTPONED TWICE, OPERATION 'OVERLORD' IS FINALLY LAUNCHED.

GENTLEMAN, THE TIME HAS COME... LET'S GO!

*ON Y VA!

The Resistance enters the scene

FOR MONTHS, THE FRENCH RESISTANCE HAS BEEN PREPARING FOR THE LANDINGS. THEY ARE WAITING FOR A SIGNAL ON THE RADIO BROADCAST FROM LONDON.
HURRY UP, PUT THE RADIO ON...
... WE'RE GOING TO MISS THE BBC MESSAGES.

THEN ONE DAY, AMONG DOZENS OF OTHER CODED MESSAGES, THEY HEAR THE LONG-AWAITED VERSE BY THE POET VERLAINE, 'LES SANGLOTS LONGS DES VIOLONS DE L'AUTOMNE...*'
'LES DÉS SONT SUR LE TAPIS... IL FAIT CHAUD À SUEZ... BLESSENT MON CŒUR D'UNE LANGUEUR MONOTONE...'
DID YOU HEAR THAT!? IT'S THE SECOND PART OF THE MESSAGE. THAT MEANS...

... THE LANDINGS ARE ON... I CAN HARDLY BELIEVE IT...

THE SABOTAGE PLANS ARE READY. EACH GROUP KNOWS EXACTLY WHAT TO DO...
BAOUMMMM

THE 'VERT**' PLAN MEANS THEY ARE TO SABOTAGE THE RAILWAY LINES.
BAOOOMMMM
VIVE LA FRANCE!

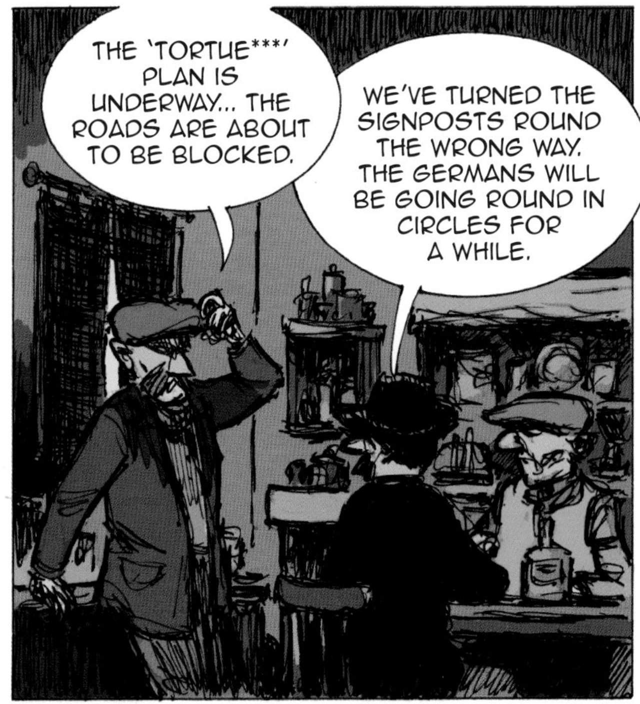
THE 'TORTUE***' PLAN IS UNDERWAY... THE ROADS ARE ABOUT TO BE BLOCKED.
WE'VE TURNED THE SIGNPOSTS ROUND THE WRONG WAY. THE GERMANS WILL BE GOING ROUND IN CIRCLES FOR A WHILE.

*VERSES FROM THE POEM 'CHANSON D'AUTOMNE' BY THE FRENCH POET, PAUL VERLAINE. – **GREEN – ***TORTOISE

The Allies bombard the Atlantic Wall

ON THE NIGHT OF THE 5TH TO THE 6TH OF JUNE, THE BOMBER PLANES TAKE OFF FROM ENGLAND. THEIR TARGET: NORMANDY!

DESTINATION: THE ATLANTIC WALL!
A FEW TONNES OF BOMBS ON THEIR HEADS, THAT SHOULD WAKE THEM UP.

THE AIM OF THESE BOMBARDMENTS IS TO DESTROY THE GUNS ALONG THE ATLANTIC WALL BEFORE ANY TROOPS LAND.

BAOOM
I'M GLAD I'M NOT UNDERNEATH... THEY'RE BEING GIVEN QUITE A SHAKE...
BAOOUM

BUT THAT NIGHT, THE SKY IS CLOUDY AND THE PILOTS STRUGGLE TO FIND THEIR WAY... AND THEIR TARGETS.

TUUUUUT! TUUUUUT
TO YOUR FIRING POSITIONS!

SURPRISED IN THE MIDDLE OF THE NIGHT, THE GERMANS ARE ON THE ALERT.

ANOTHER BOMBARDMENT!
YES, BUT IT'S NOT AS LONG AS THE OTHERS...

CONVINCED THE STORM WILL PREVENT THE ALLIES FROM LANDING THAT PARTICULAR NIGHT, MOST GENERALS HAVE LEFT THEIR COMMAND POSTS TO VISIT PARIS, SPEND TIME WITH THEIR WIFE IN GERMANY, OR MEET TO PLAY A GAME OF STRATEGY.

THERE'S NOTHING TO WORRY ABOUT. THE SEA'S TOO ROUGH...

The parachutists' tough mission

ON THE NIGHT OF THE 5TH TO THE 6TH OF JUNE, THE BRITISH AND AMERICAN PARACHUTISTS JUMP AT EITHER EXTREMITY OF THE LANDING ZONE.

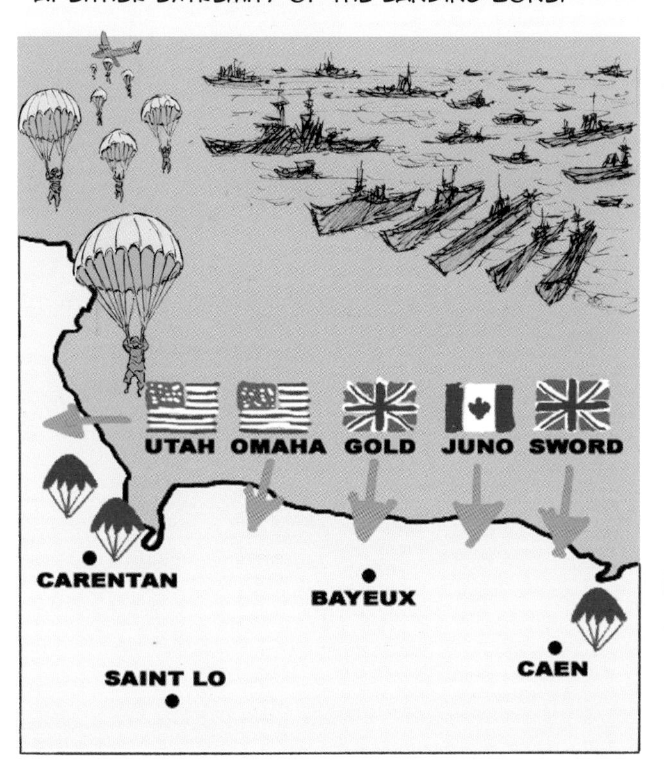
UTAH
OMAHA
GOLD
JUNO
SWORD
CARENTAN
BAYEUX
SAINT LO
CAEN

THE MEN ARE WORRIED. WILL EVERYTHING GO ACCORDING TO PLAN?

BE PROUD GUYS! YOU'LL BE THE FIRST IN NORMANDY!

WHEN IN SIGHT OF THEIR DROP ZONES, THEY JUMP, ONE AFTER ANOTHER.

THIS TIME, I'D BETTER NOT GET TANGLED UP LIKE I DID IN TRAINING.

MEANWHILE, ON THE OPPOSITE SIDE OF THE LANDING ZONE, THE BRITISH GLIDERS SILENTLY FLY OVERHEAD. THEY MUST LAND AS CLOSE AS POSSIBLE TO THE BÉNOUVILLE BRIDGE.

TARGET WITHIN SIGHT! BRACE YOURSELVES! I'M GOING TO TRY TO LAND...

... GENTLY ...
CRAAAAAAAC!!

DESPITE THE TERRIBLE DIN, AMIDST THE SILENCE OF THE NIGHT, THE BRITISH COMMANDOS SUCCESSFULLY TAKE THE GERMAN SENTRIES BY SURPRISE.

A LITTLE LATER, THE BRITISH PARACHUTISTS JUMP OVER THE MERVILLE BATTERY**. THEIR MISSION IS TO DESTROY THE GERMAN GUNS.

HAM AND JAM*! MISSION ACCOMPLISHED! THE BRIDGE IS OURS.

* HAM AND JAM: A CODED MESSAGE TO INFORM THE ALLIES OF THE SUCCESS OF THE BRITISH OPERATION.
** BATTERY: SEVERAL LARGE CALIBRE GUNS HOUSED IN BLOCKHOUSES OR PLACED ON OPEN-AIR PLATFORMS.

ON THE AMERICAN SIDE, THE PARACHUTISTS WHO JUMPED BEHIND UTAH BEACH ENCOUNTER MAJOR DIFFICULTY.

BUT, WHERE ARE ALL THE OTHERS?
PLOUF
PLOUF

WE'RE LOST. WHAT DO WE DO NOW?
USE YOUR CRICKET, THEY'RE SURE TO HEAR US.

BUT THE GERMANS CAN HEAR THE CRICKETS TOO!

CLIC
CLAC
HALT!
HANDS IN THE AIR!

AMERICAN PARAS HAVE JUMPED ON THE VILLAGE OF SAINTE-MÈRE-ÉGLISE, NOT FAR FROM UTAH BEACH.

BE CAREFUL! THERE! BEHIND THE CHURCH!
PAN
PAN
PAN!

THE PARAS LAND AS BEST THEY CAN. PRIVATE JOHN STEELE IS HANGING FROM THE CHURCH SPIRE.

QUICK! I NEED TO GET OUT OF HERE, OR I'LL BE A TARGET FOR THE GERMANS.

5 IN THE MORNING... THE US PARAS HAVE TAKEN CONTROL OF SAINTE-MÈRE-ÉGLISE. THE STAR-SPANGLED BANNER IS FLYING IN FRONT OF THE VILLAGE HALL.

MAYBE WE JUST LIBERATED THE FIRST VILLAGE IN FRANCE...

Utah Beach

UTAH BEACH, 4 AM. THE BOATS HAVE ANCHORED 20 KILOMETRES OFF SHORE. FAR ENOUGH NOT TO BE WITHIN THE GERMAN GUNS' FIRING RANGE.

IT'S TIME FOR THE MEN TO BOARD THE LANDING BARGES.

HEY! GENTLY! YOU'RE IN A HURRY TO GO AND FIGHT!
I'M JUST IN A HURRY TO SET FOOT ON SOLID GROUND. I'VE BEEN SEASICK FOR THE PAST TWO DAYS...

5 AM, THE ASSAULT IS LAUNCHED.

MEANWHILE, THE GERMAN DEFENDERS...

SIR! LOOK! BOATS STRAIGHT AHEAD!
IT CAN'T BE THE LANDINGS. THE WEATHER'S TOO BAD...

THE LANDING BARGES ARE STILL FAR FROM THE SHORE, WHEN A DELUGE OF GUNFIRE HITS THE GERMAN DEFENCES.

ON YOU GO GUYS... CLEAR THE WAY FOR US...

6.30 AM. NAVAL ARTILLERY FIRE HAS CEASED. THE BEACH LANDINGS CAN BEGIN.

THOUSANDS OF SOLDIERS LAND. AMONG THEM, GENERAL ROOSEVELT*, AN OLD AND SICK GENERAL, UNWILLING TO LEAVE HIS YOUNG SOLDIERS.
MY FIRST PRIORITY IS NOT TO GET KILLED!
CAREFUL NOT TO WET YOUR GUN. ARMS UP!

BE CAREFUL WHERE YOU WALK! IT'S MINED!

THE SERIOUSLY WOUNDED TAKE THE FIRST BOAT BACK TO ENGLAND.
HE'S BEEN SHOT IN THE LEG. HE NEEDS TO BE EVACUATED.

GENERAL ROOSEVELT HAS A TERRIBLE DOUBT... SOMETHING'S WRONG.
HOW IN THE WORLD? WE'RE IN THE WRONG PLACE!?
LOOK SIR, THE CURRENTS HAVE DRIVEN US SOUTHWARDS.

HEY GUYS, YOU'VE LANDED OVER A MILE FROM YOUR TARGET ZONE, BUT WHATEVER! THE WAR STARTS HERE.

*THEODORE ROOSEVELT WAS THE COUSIN OF THE US PRESIDENT DURING WORLD WAR II - FRANKLIN ROOSEVELT. IN 1944, HE WAS AGED 57 AND HIS HEART WAS FAILING. HE DIED A FEW WEEKS LATER.

IN THE US 4TH DIVISION, AMERICAN INDIANS WERE ENTRUSTED WITH TRANSMITTING CODED MESSAGES IN COMANCHE LANGUAGE.

WE HAVE LANDED. BUT WE'RE IN THE WRONG PLACE. PLEASE PASS ON!
TSAAKU NUNNUWEE... ATAHTU NUNNUWEE...

THE ENGINEERS MUST NOW CLEAR THE BEACH, SO THAT REINFORCEMENTS CAN LAND.

CLEAR ALL THAT AWAY WITH A BULLDOZER.

AS SOON AS THE WALL HAS BEEN DESTROYED, WE'LL SEND THE TANKS THROUGH.

IN THE AFTERNOON, THE 4TH DIVISION JOINS THE PARACHUTISTS WHO HAVE JUMPED BY NIGHT. MISSION ACCOMPLISHED!

HOW MANY MEN HAVE WE LOST?
AROUND 200 SIR.

THE GERMAN PRISONERS ARE GATHERED TOGETHER BEHIND BARBED WIRING.

THE WAR IS OVER FOR US.
DO YOU THINK THEY'RE GOING TO TAKE US TO ENGLAND?

MEANWHILE, REINFORCEMENTS COME FLOODING IN...

Omaha Beach

OMAHA BEACH ON THE NIGHT OF THE 5TH TO 6TH OF JUNE. HUNDREDS OF TONNES OF BOMBS ARE DROPPED ON THE GERMAN DEFENCES.

WE CAN'T SEE ANYTHING. TOO MUCH CLOUD.

AT DAWN, THE NAVAL ARTILLERY* CAN'T SEE MUCH EITHER. IT FIRES, BUT INACCURATELY.
TOO MUCH SMOKE... BUT WITH THE THRASHING WE GAVE THEM LAST NIGHT...
... THERE CAN'T BE MUCH LEFT OF THE GERMANS.

BAOUUMM

LADEN WITH MEN, THE BARGES ARE PUT TO THE WATER AT AROUND 4 AM. THEY MOVE TOWARDS THE BEACHES.

I'M COLD... AND I'M SOAKED.

MOST OF THE AMPHIBIOUS TANKS THAT WERE TO COVER THE FIRST WAVES OF ASSAULT HAVE SUNK, ALONG WITH THEIR CREWS.

SCOOP! SCOOP! WE'RE GONNA SINK!
I'M DOING MY BEST. THE WAVES ARE TOO STRONG.

BLUP!

*GUNS INSTALLED ABOARD THE SHIPS.

6.30 AM. THE FIRST WAVE OF ASSAULT RUSHES ONTO THE BEACH. SPARED BY THE NIGHT AND EARLY MORNING BOMBINGS, THE GERMANS FIRE BURSTS AT THE AMERICAN SOLDIERS WITH THEIR MACHINE GUNS.
RUN BUDDIES! RUN!

IN 5 MINUTES, 90% OF THE FIRST WAVE OF ASSAULT IS ANNIHILATED. CARNAGE...

ONE WAVE OF ASSAULT FOLLOWS ANOTHER. THE BEACH IS A SCENE OF TOTAL CHAOS.
THERE ARE TWO KINDS OF PEOPLE WHO ARE STAYING ON THIS BEACH, THOSE WHO ARE DEAD AND THOSE WHO ARE GOING TO DIE. NOW LET'S GET THE HELL OUT OF HERE!

THE GERMAN GUNS INSTALLED ON THE CLIFFS ABOVE THE BEACH OFFER THE DEFENDERS A CLEAR ADVANTAGE.
THOSE AMERICANS WEREN'T EXPECTING THAT, WERE THEY?
HA ! HA
SHUT UP AND FIRE.

THE AMERICANS WHO HAVE MANAGED TO CROSS THE BEACH TAKE SHELTER BEHIND AN ANTITANK WALL. OTHERS ARE CROUCHING AT THE FOOT OF A LINE OF PEBBLES.

WE'RE SAFE HERE. WE CAN TAKE A BREATHER.

THE MEDICAL TEAMS DO THEIR BEST TO PROVIDE FIRST AID TO THE WOUNDED.
OVER THERE, A GUY'S BEEN HIT. LET'S GO!

8.30AM. FROM THE DECK OF THE CRUISER USS AUGUSTA, GENERAL BRADLEY, COMMANDER OF THE OPERATION, NERVOUSLY OBSERVES THE BATTLE.

IT'S A CATASTROPHE! LET'S STOP SENDING REINFORCEMENTS TO OMAHA AND SEND THEM TO UTAH, THE SITUATION'S BETTER THERE...

THE AMERICANS ARE STRUGGLING TO ADVANCE. WE NEED TO MAKE A DECISION, AND RISK OUR ALL.
ORDER FOR THE SHIPS TO APPROACH AS CLOSE AS POSSIBLE TO THE BEACH AND TO FIRE AT POINT BLANK RANGE.
IT'S RISKY... BUT IF IT WORKS... IT'LL SAVE US.

BAOUUUUUM

BULL'S EYE!

LATE MORNING, MORE BREAKTHROUGHS ARE MADE. THE AMERICANS ARE ADVANCING AT LAST!

TA TATATATA

TA TATATATA TA TATATATA
COLLEVILLE! STRAIGHT AHEAD! LET'S GO BUDDIES!

LOOK OUT! THEY'RE ATTACKING FROM THE REAR!
TA TATATATA

BY LATE AFTERNOON, THE BEACH IS UNDER CONTROL. REINFORCEMENTS CAN LAND.

ON THE EVENING OF THE 6TH OF JUNE, 30,000 MEN HAVE LANDED. 3,000 ARE OUT OF ACTION. A HEAVY TOLL FOR JUST ONE DAY!

WHAT A HORRIFIC DAY! ALL THOSE MEN KILLED, DROWNED, WOUNDED...

IT IS ON OMAHA BEACH THAT THE LANDINGS HAVE BEEN THE TOUGHEST, AND DEATHS THE HIGHEST. LATER, THEY WILL CALL IT 'BLOODY OMAHA'

WE'RE IN A PRECARIOUS POSITION. THE ENEMY CAN COUNTER-ATTACK AT ANY TIME.
I HOPE THINGS WENT BETTER ON THE OTHER BEACHES...

Pointe du Hoc

6 AM, OFF POINTE DU HOC. COLONEL RUDDER HAS GROUPED TOGETHER HIS RANGERS. TO GIVE THEM ONE LAST MESSAGE.

NOW LISTEN RANGERS! LET'S SHOW THEM WHAT YOU'RE WORTH... DEPART IN 5 MINUTES. GOOD LUCK GUYS!

THE MISSION ENTRUSTED TO THE 225 RANGERS IS TO DESTROY THE GUNS INSTALLED AT THE SUMMIT OF POINTE DU HOC.

WE'VE BEEN SOAKING FOR HOURS. I'M FROZEN. ARE YOU NOT?
DON'T WORRY. I THINK WE'LL SOON BE ABLE TO WARM UP!

THE RANGERS ADVANCE ALONGSIDE THE CLIFFS, SHELTERED FROM ENEMY GUNFIRE BY A SMOKE SCREEN.

WE'VE DRIFTED SIR... IT'S THE WRONG HEADLAND! HOC IS BEHIND US...

7 AM. AFTER MAKING A U-TURN, THE RANGERS FINALLY SPOT POINTE DU HOC. BUT THE GERMANS HAVE HAD TIME TO SOUND THE ALERT

TATATATATA

THE RANGERS FINALLY SET FOOT ON SOLID GROUND AND, FOR THEM, THE HARDEST IS YET TO COME...

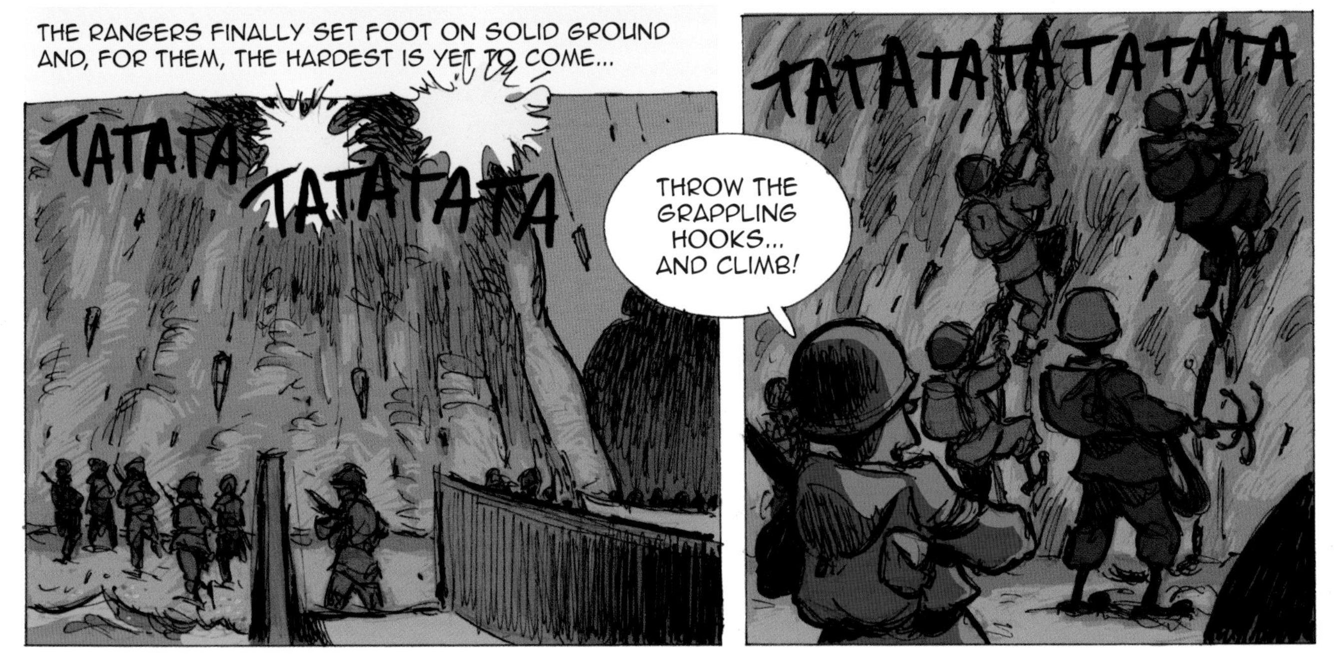
TATATA
TATATATA
TATATATATATATATA
THROW THE GRAPPLING HOOKS... AND CLIMB!

THE ROPES ARE WET AND TOO HEAVY. THEY KEEP FALLING...

SOME RANGERS TRY TO SCALE THE CLIFF BARE-HANDED, HOLLOWING OUT HOLDS WITH THEIR KNIVES.

ONCE AT THE SUMMIT, A NASTY SURPRISE AWAITS THEM.
HURRY UP! WE MUST DESTROY THE GUNS!
CAREFUL! THEY'RE STILL FIRING!

LOOK AT THAT, GUYS! THERE ARE NO GUNS! THEY'RE JUST WOODEN STAKES!
WE DID ALL THAT FOR NOTHING!?

THIS IS RUDDER, HOC IS UNDER CONTROL... I NEED REINFORCEMENTS AND AMMUNITION... HEAVY LOSSES!

MORNING OF 7TH JUNE. THE REQUESTED REINFORCEMENTS NEVER ARRIVE. THEY ARE SENT TO OMAHA.
WE'RE GOING TO BE SHORT ON AMMUNITION AND FOOD, BUT WE'LL HAVE TO HOLD OUT. AN ORDER'S AN ORDER.

MORNING OF 8TH JUNE. REINFORCEMENTS ARRIVE AT LAST!
WELL, WE'D BETTER START LOOKING FOR THOSE GUNS NOW! THEY MUST BE SOMEWHERE.

Gold Beach

THE GUNS ABOARD THE SHIPS HAVE BEEN FIRING AT THE GERMAN DEFENCES FOR AN HOUR. IT'S 6.30 IN THE MORNING.

CURSE IT! THE LONGUES BATTERY IS STILL FIRING...

THE BRITISH TROOPS LAND ON GOLD BEACH. SHORTLY AFTER 6 AM, THE BARGES ARE PUT TO THE WATER, 7 KILOMETRES FROM THE COAST.

WE'LL BE THERE IN AN HOUR...
I'M SCARED ...

30 MINUTES BEFORE THE ASSAULT, FROGMEN CLEAR THE ACCESS CHANNELS OF MINES.

LADEN WITH THEIR WEAPONS AND THEIR KIT, THE SOLDIERS WHO FALL INTO THE WATER ARE AT GREAT RISK OF DROWNING.

WE'RE SINKING! JUMP!
WE'RE TOO HEAVY! WE'RE GOING TO DROWN!

TATATATATATATATA

7.15 AM. THE FIRST WAVE OF ASSAULT ARRIVES.

TATATATATA
FASTER! THEY'RE FIRING FROM ALL SIDES!
TAKE SHELTER BEHIND THE TANKS.

THE FUNNY* TANKS ALSO MAKE THE JOURNEY. THE 'CRABS' ARE AMONG THE FIRST TO LAND AND TO CLEAR THE WAY THROUGH THE MINEFIELDS.

BAOUM

LET'S TAKE THEM FROM THE REAR.
BAOUM

A BRITISH COMMANDO SETS OF TO JOIN FORCES WITH THE AMERICANS LANDED ON OMAHA.

IF WE FIND EACH OTHER, WE HAVE A CHANCE.

AT AROUND 11 AM, THE BRITISH CAN FINALLY LEAVE THE BEACH, FREEING SPACE FOR REINFORCEMENTS TO ARRIVE.

WE'RE TO HEAD FOR THE HEIGHTS AT PORT-EN-BESSIN.

NEARBY, THE BRITISH ARE SURPRISED TO SEE GERMAN TANKS ARRIVE, TO FIND OUT WHAT IS GOING ON.

ON THE EVENING OF THE 6TH OF JUNE, THE BRITISH ARE IN CONTROL OF A LARGE SECTOR. AN OFFICER REPORTS TO HIS SUPERIORS.

U-TURN, GUYS. BACK TO BASE TO REPORT.
STRANGE THOUGH, ALL THOSE BRITS.
25,000 SOLDIERS LANDED... 400 MEN OUT OF ACTION...
OUR TROOPS ARE ON THE OUTSKIRTS OF BAYEUX.
GOOD JOB WE HAD THE FUNNIES... THAT WAS SOME GREAT IDEA, GENERAL HOBART*!

*FUNNIES WERE INVENTED BY GENERAL HOBART. THEY WERE CURIOUS AND APPROPRIATELY NAMED TANKS EQUIPPED WITH CHAINS, DESIGNED TO BLOW UP MINES (CRAB TANK) OR WITH A SHORT GUN TO DESTROY WALLS (PETARD TANK).

Juno Beach

OVER THE NIGHT, NOT FAR FROM JUNO BEACH, ALLIED PLANES BOMBARD THE ATLANTIC WALL.

SIR, THEY'RE BOMBING HARDER THAN USUAL.
YES... IT'S GOING TO BE A LONG NIGHT...

AFTER THE NIGHT-TIME BOMBINGS AND THE NAVAL ARTILLERY FIRE, THE CANADIANS PREPARE TO LAND. THE ASSAULT IS SCHEDULED FOR 7.35 AM. BUT THE OPERATION IS RUNNING LATE

OH MY GOD... I'M SEASICK...
SHUT UP AND SCOOP!

THE SEA IS WILD OFF JUNO BEACH. THE WAVES ARE HUGE AND THE ROCKS HINDER ACCESS TO THE BEACH.

WATCH OUT! WE'RE HEADING STRAIGHT FOR THE GERMAN DEFENCES!
SWERVE RIGHT!

BAOUUMM

BLUP!
BLURP
BLUP

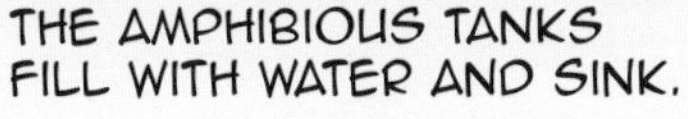
THE AMPHIBIOUS TANKS FILL WITH WATER AND SINK.

THEY'RE HEADING STRAIGHT FOR THE GERMAN DEFENCES. IT'S GONNA BE CARNAGE!

THE ASSAULT IS DELAYED. THE SEA IS TOO ROUGH. THE MINE CLEARERS CAN'T DO THEIR JOB.

WE'RE GOING TO APPROACH AS CLOSE AS POSSIBLE AND LAND THE TANKS DIRECT ON THE BEACH.

IT'S RISKY, BUT, IF WE DON'T, THEY'RE ALL GOING TO SINK.

THIS DELAY LEAVES THE GERMANS ENOUGH TIME TO MAN THEIR FIRING POSITIONS.

LET'S WAIT TILL THEY DRAW CLOSER BEFORE OPENING FIRE.

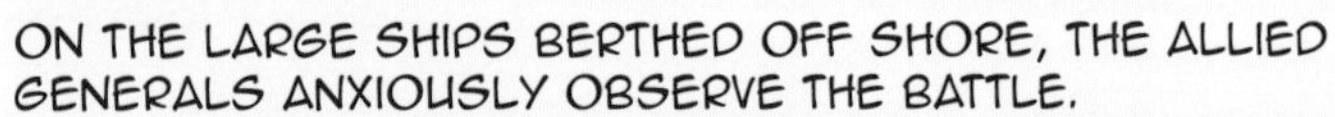
ON THE LARGE SHIPS BERTHED OFF SHORE, THE ALLIED GENERALS ANXIOUSLY OBSERVE THE BATTLE.

IT'S A CATASTROPHE! THE TANKS ARE SO LATE THAT THE MEN HAVE LANDED BEFORE THEM.

THEY HAVE NO MEANS OF PROTECTION. THEY'RE GONNA GET KILLED.

ON THE BEACH, THE CANADIANS ARE STOPPED IN THEIR TRACKS BY A SEA WALL DEFENDED BY GERMANS.

TATATATA TATA TA
BUT, WHERE ARE THE TANKS?!
HERE'S HOPING THEY DIDN'T ALL SINK...

THE TANKS ARE HERE, AT LAST! THEY'RE GOING TO OPEN BREACHES IN THE WALL.

IT'S HIGH TIME!

LET'S GO!

THE BEACH IS CLUTTERED WITH TANKS, WOUNDED SOLDIERS, VEHICLES AND MATERIAL LEFT BEHIND BY THE CANADIANS. AS THE TIDE RISES, THE SITUATION WORSENS.

WE NEED TO CLEAR ALL THAT, AND FAST. THE TIDE'S RISING. REINFORCEMENTS ARE ON THEIR WAY.

TOO LATE SIR. WE DON'T HAVE THE TIME!

ON JUNO BEACH TOO, THE LANDINGS HAVE BEEN DIFFICULT.
WE HAVEN'T ACCOMPLISHED ALL OUR AIMS, BUT IT COULD'VE BEEN WORSE.

WE'RE GOING TO TRY TO FIND THE BRITISH UNITS LANDED ON GOLD BEACH.

THE CANADIANS LIBERATE VILLAGES ACROSS THE COUNTRYSIDE. THEIR OBJECTIVE IS TO CAPTURE THE AIRPORT AT CARPIQUET, NEAR CAEN.
N'AYEZ PAS PEUR*.
BUT... YOU SPEAK FRENCH?

YES, WE'RE FROM QUEBEC!
HEY! COME AND HAVE A GLASS OF CIDER, YOU DESERVE IT.

AT HIGH TIDE, THE BOAT LADEN WITH PRISONERS TAKES TO THE SEA TO HEAD FOR ENGLAND.

THE BEACH IS CALM AGAIN.

*DON'T BE AFRAID!

Sword Beach

ON SWORD BEACH, THE BRITISH TROOPS ARE PREPARING TO LAND.

THIS DARN STORM IS GOING TO MAKE US LATE.
IMPOSSIBLE! ORDERS ARE ORDERS. THE LANDINGS ARE SCHEDULED FOR PRECISELY 7.25 AM.

THE KING OF ENGLAND IS NEVER LATE, AS FAR AS I KNOW! WELL, NEITHER ARE WE! SIMPLE MATTER OF GOOD MANNERS.

THE ALLIED GENERALS HAVE DECIDED TO HAVE THE FUNNIES LAND FIRST, TO DESTROY THE GERMAN DEFENCES BEFORE THE TROOPS ARRIVE.

BAOUUMMMM

7 IN THE MORNING. PUT TO THE WATER FAR FROM THE COAST, THE BARGES NOW HEAD FOR THE BEACH...

WE NEED TO SPOT THE CHURCH SPIRE... THE ONE ON THE PHOTOGRAPHS WE SAW DURING TRAINING.
I CAN'T SEE ANYTHING FOR THE SMOKE...

WHEN THE BRITISH TROOPS ARRIVE, THEY ARE WELCOMED BY GUNFIRE FROM ALL SIDES.

AHHH!!

IN THE BRITISH RANKS, A CURIOUS CHARACTER IS PREPARING TO LAND AND TO LEAD HIS COMMANDO. HE IS LORD LOVAT, A SCOT WHO LANDS IN THE COMPANY OF BILL, HIS LOYAL BAGPIPE PLAYER.

PLAY 'HIGHLAND LADDIE*' FOR US, IT'LL BOOST THE MEN'S MORALE.

ONE OF THE COMMANDOS LATER REPORTS THAT, AS HE PLAYS, THE GERMANS STOP FIRING FOR A MOMENT...

... BUT JUST FOR A MOMENT...

WE NEED TO CLEAR THE BEACH AND OPEN BREACHES IN THE GERMAN DEFENCES, SO THAT THE TROOPS CAN ENTER THE TOWN.

TATATATATA
LOOK! THEY'VE TRANSFORMED HOLIDAY HOMES INTO BLOCKHOUSES**!
LOOK OUT! ONE OF THEM HAS SPOTTED US!

*IT WAS A SCOTTISH TRADITION TO LEAD MEN INTO COMBAT TO THE SOUND OF THE BAGPIPES... HOWEVER, SINCE IT WAS EXTREMELY DANGEROUS, IT WAS FORBIDDEN TO DO SO AFTER WORLD WAR I.

** CONCRETE SHELTERS BUILT BY THE GERMANS TO HOUSE GUNS AND FOR DEFENSIVE PURPOSES.

THE TIDE IS RISING AND, JUST LIKE ON JUNO BEACH, THE BEACH HAS BECOME INCREASINGLY CLUTTERED WITH EXPLODED TANKS, BURNED VEHICLES, DESTROYED MATERIAL AND WOUNDED TROOPS...

IF YOU DON'T GET OUT OF HERE FAST, WE'RE GOING TO GET TRAPPED.

FIGHTING RESUMES, MORE VIOLENTLY THAN BEFORE...

TATATATATATATATATATATA!

... AND THE 177 MEN FROM THE KIEFFER COMMANDO, WHO LANDED WITH THE BRITISH TROOPS, LAUNCH THEIR ASSAULT.

OUR COMMANDER'S BEEN HIT IN THE LEG!
I'M OK! I CAN KEEP GOING!

ONCE AT THE FOOT OF THE DUNE, THE MEN GATHER TOGETHER TO TAKE STOCK OF THE SITUATION.

WE NEED TO GET PAST THE BARBED WIRE...

... THEN, WE CAN ENTER OUISTREHAM.

TO DESTROY THE BARBED WIRE, THE BRITISH USE LONG TUBES IN WHICH THEY PLACE EXPLOSIVES: THEY'RE CALLED BANGALORES.

ON YOU GO... DETONATE!
I'M TRYING! IT WAS MUCH EASIER DURING TRAINING... THERE WERE NO GERMANS FIRING AT US.

AT AROUND MIDDAY, THE BEACH IS FINALLY CLEARED AND SEVERAL BREACHES HAVE BEEN OPENED FOR TROOPS TO MOVE INLAND.

NOW, WE NEED TO CLEAR THE TOWN!
EASIER SAID THAN DONE, WITH ALL THESE STREETS AND ALL THESE HOUSES.

OUISTREHAM AND ITS CASINO, TRANSFORMED INTO A BLOCKHOUSE BY THE GERMANS, ARE CAPTURED AFTER FIERCE COMBAT.
THE GERMANS EVENTUALLY GIVE UP FIGHTING, WITH THE EXCEPTION OF A FEW GROUPS, WHICH CONTINUE TO RESIST.
ON WE GO GUYS, TOWARDS CAEN... STAY ON THE LOOK-OUT...
BUT EVERYTHING SEEMS SO CALM.

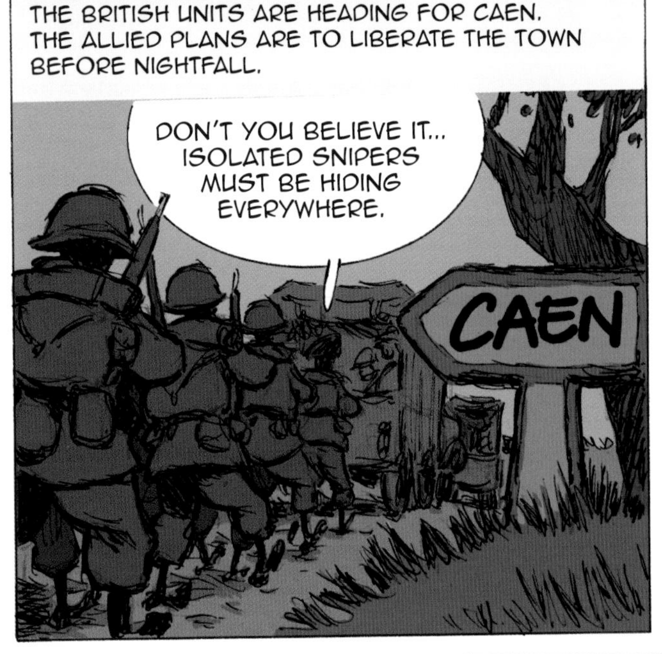
THE BRITISH UNITS ARE HEADING FOR CAEN. THE ALLIED PLANS ARE TO LIBERATE THE TOWN BEFORE NIGHTFALL.
DON'T YOU BELIEVE IT... ISOLATED SNIPERS MUST BE HIDING EVERYWHERE.
CAEN

1.32 PM. ACCORDING TO THE INITIAL PLAN, LORD LOVAT AND HIS MEN REACH BÉNOUVILLE, WHERE COMMANDOS HAVE LANDED TO CAPTURE A BRIDGE.

WE'RE 2 MINUTES 32 SECONDS LATE. WE'RE GOING TO HAVE TO APOLOGISE TO HOWARD'S PARACHUTISTS.
NOW, CAN YOU PLAY 'BLUE BONNETS OVER THE BORDER*' FOR US?

CONTRARY TO ALLIED PLANS, CAEN IS NOT LIBERATED ON THE 6TH OF JUNE. THE GERMANS PUT UP STRONG RESISTANCE IN THE SECTOR. THE TOWN IS ONLY BE CAPTURED A MONTH LATER, ON THE 9TH OF JULY.

* 18TH CENTURY SCOTTISH TUNE.

The D-Day Landings are a success

IN FRANCE, NEWS OF THE LANDINGS SPREADS FAST. AT 9.30 AM, US TIME, GENERAL EISENHOWER'S FIRST PRESS RELEASE ANNOUNCES THE OPERATION'S SUCCESS.

UNDER THE COMMAND OF GENERAL EISENHOWER, ALLIED NAVAL FORCES...

... BEGAN LANDING ALLIED ARMIES THIS MORNING ON THE NORTHERN COAST OF FRANCE.

C'EST LA LIBÉRATION*!!!!

BACK AT HITLER'S HEADQUARTERS, EVERYONE IS WORRIED, BUT NO ONE DARES WAKE THE FÜHRER TO INFORM HIM THAT, THIS TIME, THE SITUATION IS SERIOUS. WHEN HE GETS UP...

DON'T LET YOURSELF BE FOOLED BY THE ALLIES. IT'S JUST ANOTHER DIVERSION OPERATION.
BUT, THEY'VE REALLY LANDED! IN NORMANDY!

IN NORMANDY!! HA! HA! HA! AND WHY NOT ON THE BEACHES?
BUT, THAT'S EXACTLY WHAT THEY DID, MEIN FÜRHER... ON THE BEACHES...

DESPITE THE PREVIOUS NIGHT'S EVENTS, HITLER IS STILL CONVINCED THAT THE TRUE LANDINGS WILL BE IN PAS-DE-CALAIS. HE BELIEVES SO TILL JULY.

THAT'S ENOUGH. I'M TELLING YOU, THE REAL LANDING WILL BE IN NORTH-EASTERN FRANCE.
SEND A FEW REINFORCEMENTS TO NORMANDY, THAT SHOULD DO.

ON THE EVENING OF THE 6TH OF JUNE, 156,000 MEN AND 20,000 VEHICLES HAVE LANDED. ALTHOUGH 10,000 MEN ARE SADLY OUT OF ACTION (DEAD, WOUNDED OR UNACCOUNTED FOR...), THERE HAVE BEEN FEWER DEATHS THAN THE ALLIES' ESTIMATION.

*IT'S OUR LIBERATION!

THE LANDING OPERATION IS A SUCCESS BUT THE ALLIES HAVE STILL NOT REACHED ALL THEIR TARGETS AND, IN CERTAIN SECTORS - LIKE OMAHA - THE SITUATION REMAINS FRAGILE.

WHEN I THINK ABOUT THE BATTLE THAT WAS WAGED ON THAT BEACH...

... AND NOW, IT'S SO CALM...

A FEW DAYS LATER, THE BRITISH BEGIN TO BUILD AN ARTIFICIAL HARBOUR IN ARROMANCHES*. ALL THE MATERIAL, INCLUDING CONCRETE CAISSONS, HAVE BEEN TOWED OVER FROM ENGLAND.

WE'RE GOING TO SINK THE CAISSON HERE, IN LINE WITH THE OTHERS.
AND YOU RECKON THAT'LL END UP LIKE A HARBOUR?

ONCE SUNK IN A SEMI-CIRCULAR FORMATION, THE CAISSONS WILL ENABLE SHIPS TO UNLOAD THEIR CARGO, SHELTERED FROM THE WAVES.

OF COURSE! IT'S AN INGENIOUS IDEA!
OH YEAH! ANOTHER ONE OF CHURCHILL'S BRILLIANT IDEAS?

A FEW WEEKS LATER, THE HARBOUR IS EQUIPPED WITH UNLOADING PLATFORMS AND FLOATING CAUSEWAYS TO AND FROM THE SHORE.

PAN PAN PAN PAN

AND AS THE HARBOUR IS GRADUALLY INSTALLED, THE ALLIED ARMIES CONTINUE THEIR PROGRESSION TO INLAND NORMANDY. HOWEVER, THE GERMANS ARE STILL THERE, AND THEY CONTINUE TO FIGHT RELENTLESSLY.

GENERAL DE GAULLE IN TURN LANDS IN NORMANDY ON THE 14TH OF JUNE. HE TRAVELS TO BAYEUX, A SMALL TOWN, MIRACULOUSLY SPARED BY THE COMBAT. AFTER BEING ACCLAIMED BY THE LOCAL POPULATION, HE MAKES A FAMOUS SPEECH ANNOUNCING FRANCE'S LIBERATION.

AH! SO THIS IS THE FAMOUS GENERAL DE GAULLE**!

*A SECOND HARBOUR WAS BUILT AT OMAHA, BUT IT WAS SOON TO BE DESTROYED DURING A STORM.
** EVEN IF SOME FRENCH PEOPLE HAD HEARD HIS VOICE, NO ONE HAD EVER SEEN HIM.

6th June 1944: THE NORMANDY LANDINGS

Text by Isabelle Bournier

WHO WERE THE ALLIES?

The Allies comprised Great Britain, the United States, Canada and Russia (at the time called the USSR). In 1942 and 1943, the leaders of these States met and finally agreed to organise a landing operation in Normandy. In December 1943, an American general was named to command the Allied armies: General Eisenhower.

WINSTON CHURCHILL
(1874-1965)

© IWM.

Winston Churchill was appointed British Prime Minister in 1940. He refused to let Hitler's armies invade Britain and encouraged the British people to resist. He was an ally for the United States and it was in Britain that the landing operation was to be prepared.

BERNARD MONTGOMERY
(1887-1976)

© IWM.

The British were already familiar with General Montgomery. He was famous for having led his troops to a great victory in North Africa (the Desert War in 1943). But he was also renowned for being ill-tempered. During the Normandy Landings, he was in command of land forces. His men nicknamed him 'Monty'.

FRANKLIN DELANO ROOSEVELT
(1882-1945)

CBS

© IWM.

He was the President of the United States. He played a highly important role in his country's entry into the War and helped the British to prepare for the Normandy Landings by supplying military material and troops. He sent American soldiers to Europe to fight against Nazi Germany and, at the same time, fought against the Japanese in Asia.

CHARLES DE GAULLE
(1890-1970)

In 1940, General de Gaulle was a sort of War Minister in France. When the German army invaded France, he refused to accept defeat. He left for London and called upon the French people to resist. Young French citizens came to join him and he created a new army: the Free French Forces, which took part in the landing operation in Normandy. In 1944, General de Gaulle returned to France. He became President of the French Republic.

DWIGHT DAVID EISENHOWER
(1890-1969)

© IWM.

General Dwight Eisenhower was the chief of the Allied armies. He had already organised landings in North Africa, in 1942, and in Sicily, in 1943. He was relatively unknown but boasted excellent human qualities. He was calm, intelligent and had a talent for settling disputes between his generals who did not always agree. After the war, he became President of the United States. He was nicknamed 'Ike'.

© IWM.

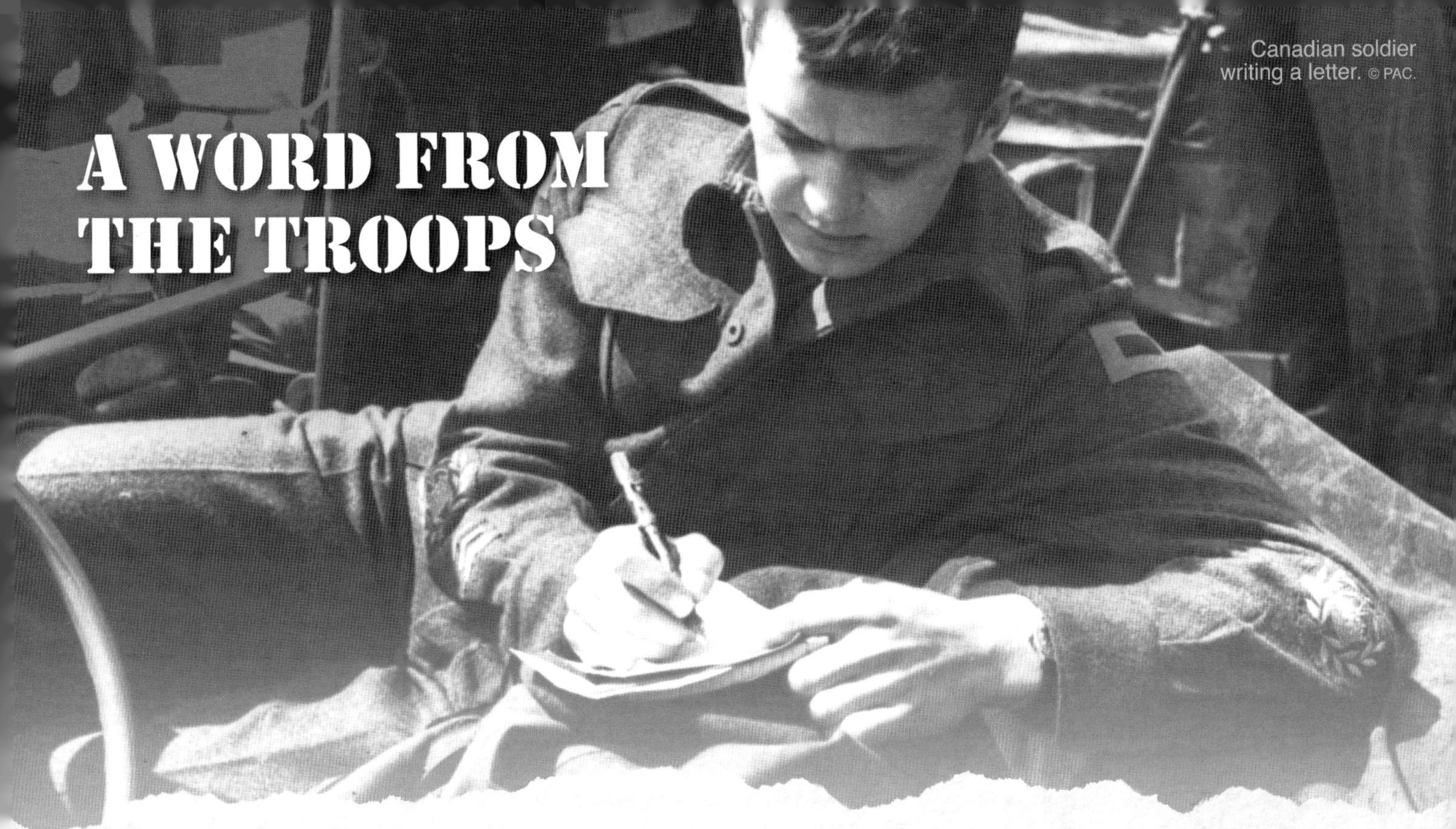
Canadian soldier writing a letter. © PAC.

A WORD FROM THE TROOPS

Many soldiers wrote letters or filled their diaries during or after the Battle of Normandy. They told of the violence of the combat, their sadness at being far from their families and their fear of dying.

'The sky lit up with explosions, some of them in a huge clamour. The bombs dropped by the planes, the shells fired by the ships, the rockets whistling over our heads, the German gunfire [...]. It was a terrifying spectacle! As we approached the beach, we began to make out the shoreline. The shells fired from the boats made geysers spurt up from the sea. We kept our heads low.'

Bruce Bradley, American soldier on Omaha Beach.

'The ramps were lowered. We could see what it looked like, 6 miles of water between us and the beach. [...] In a nutshell, we were in the water at last. In the breakers. The time had come to remember all we'd learned on how to walk in this water, and how to hold our rifles high, so they didn't get wet. Foot after foot, we advanced. In front of me, there was smoke, noise. We'd never heard anything like it. It was so different from training! This time, it was really happening!'

Cliff Bowering, Canadian soldier on Juno Beach.

'We were surrounded by mines [...] and I was expecting to get blown up at any time.'

Alfred, landing barge pilot on Juno Beach.

'Suddenly, through a tear in the smoke, the underwater defences, stakes and crossed steel bars intermingling with barbed wire, surged up before us. We were close to our target. A bang, our barges had just landed. [...]. Donning their green berets, the first group rushed onto the beach, but a few instants before the second group thrust forth, a 75mm shell blew up the ramp in a clamour of splitting wood and metal. The most important question was, 'Are we in front of our landing point?'

Philippe Kieffer, commander of a French battalion on Sword Beach.

'At 1.30am, the alarm was sounded: we had been bombarded by the Americans to our right and our left. We waited, attentive, anxious, our weapons beside us. At dawn, at around 4 am, we began to make out the outline of the first big enemy ships. [...]. Lightning bolts were fired from their guns at an infernal rate. Soon, the first shells came down on us in a diabolical din. The bombs dropped by the planes continued to whistle past.'

Franz Gockel, a German soldier on Omaha Beach.

6TH JUNE 1944: THE ALLIED ARMIES LAND IN NORMANDY

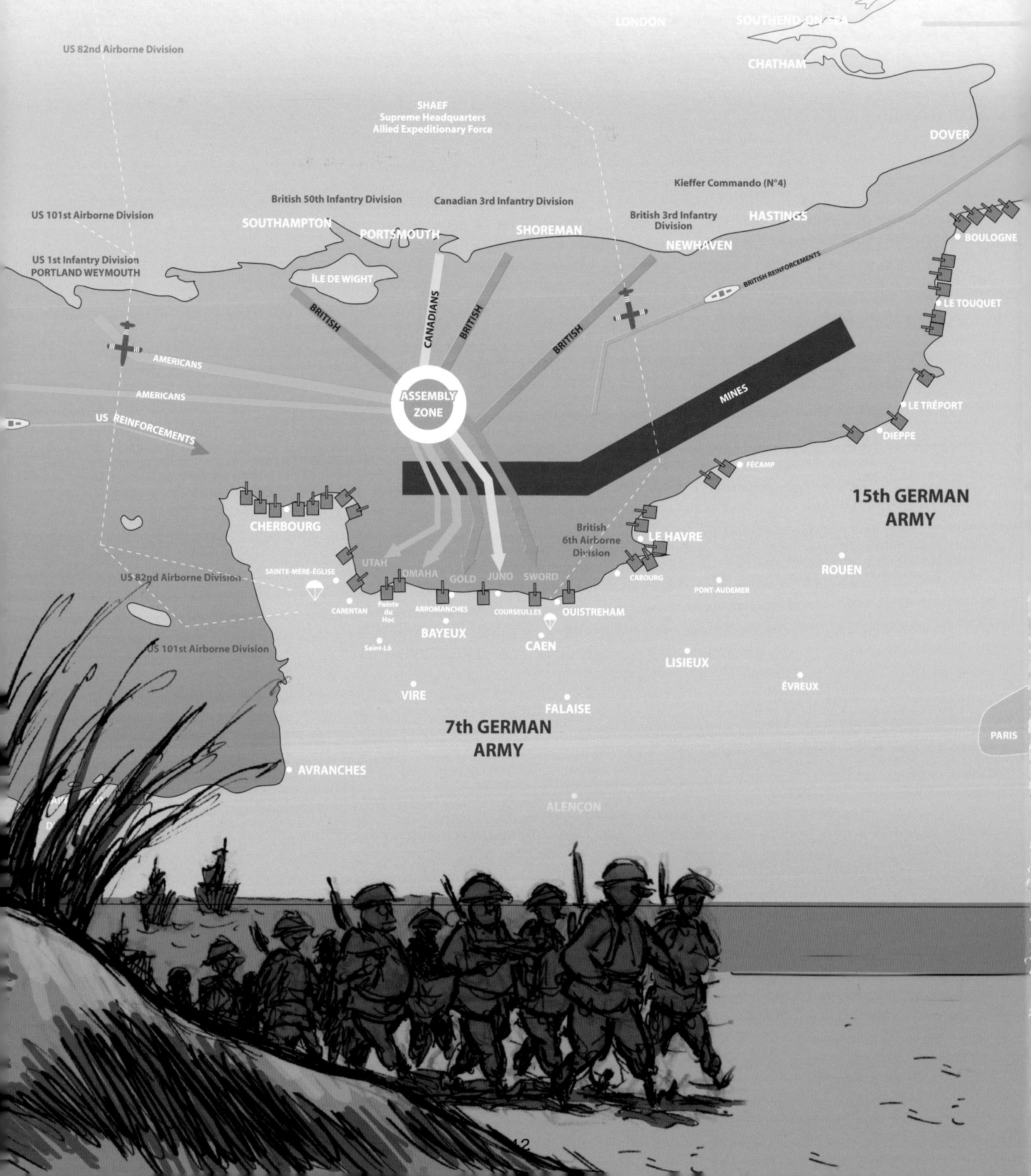

LONDON
SOUTHEND-ON-SEA
CHATHAM
US 82nd Airborne Division
SHAEF
Supreme Headquarters
Allied Expeditionary Force
DOVER
Kieffer Commando (N°4)
British 50th Infantry Division
Canadian 3rd Infantry Division
British 3rd Infantry Division
US 101st Airborne Division
SOUTHAMPTON
PORTSMOUTH
SHOREMAN
HASTINGS
NEWHAVEN
BOULOGNE
US 1st Infantry Division
PORTLAND WEYMOUTH
ÎLE DE WIGHT
BRITISH REINFORCEMENTS
BRITISH
CANADIANS
BRITISH
BRITISH
LE TOUQUET
AMERICANS
AMERICANS
ASSEMBLY ZONE
MINES
US REINFORCEMENTS
LE TRÉPORT
DIEPPE
FÉCAMP
15th GERMAN ARMY
CHERBOURG
British
6th Airborne
Division
LE HAVRE
UTAH
OMAHA
GOLD
JUNO
SWORD
ROUEN
SAINTE-MÈRE-ÉGLISE
US 82nd Airborne Division
CABOURG
PONT-AUDEMER
CARENTAN
Pointe du Hoc
ARROMANCHES
COURSEULLES
OUISTREHAM
BAYEUX
CAEN
Saint-Lô
US 101st Airborne Division
LISIEUX
ÉVREUX
VIRE
FALAISE
7th GERMAN ARMY
PARIS
AVRANCHES
ALENÇON

THE 4 PHASES OF THE LANDING OPERATION

The landings required months of preparation and troop training. Nothing was left to chance; however, on the 6th of June 1944, everything didn't quite go according to plan...

American bomber planes with their black and white invasion strips used to recognise Allied planes.
© NARA /Cherbourg Municipal Library.

1/ The Allies bombarded the Atlantic Wall

On the night of the 5th to the 6th of June, before having thousands of soldiers land on the beaches, the Allies bombarded the German defences along the Atlantic Wall. Unfortunately, they failed to destroy all of the German guns. At dawn, some of them were still capable of firing

American parachutists, their faces blackened for camouflage.
© NARA

2/ The parachutists jumped by night

At around midnight, American and British parachutists jumped on the two extremities of the landing zone. The Americans were dropped behind Utah Beach, to the west. The British parachutists jumped to the east, behind Sword Beach. Their kit bag weighed over 50 kilogrammes.

Naval artillery fire.
© NARA

3/ The naval artillery fired on the Atlantic Wall

Early in the morning, the boats began to fire on the German defences. The Allies ships and the German guns engaged in an artillery duel. The resulting noise was deafening.

4/ The men landed on the beaches

Meanwhile, the soldiers boarded their landing barges (small boats). Tossed by the waves, they approached the coast before landing on the beaches. The men were soaked. They were cold. Many of them suffered seasickness. The first to arrive were killed before they even had time to set foot on the sand. Under constant German gunfire, the others struggled to advance. Omaha Beach was the one with the highest number of dead.

A landing barge approaching the coast.
© NARA

THE GI AND HIS KIT BAG

GI was the name given to the American soldiers. Unlike the British soldiers, who had already fought in North Africa and in Sicily, many GIs had no military experience. But they were quick to learn how to fight...

With them, the soldiers carried the necessary weapons and material to survive several days on the front lines: a back pack, a mess tin and its pouch, a folding spade with its case, sun cream, a packet of insecticide, tablets to purify water, K-rations (canned food), paperback books, a guidebook with a few words in French, etc.

The life belt

It could be inflated automatically by emptying two small gas bottles, or by blowing into a pipe. The life jacket was intended to prevent the GI from sinking. But if he wore it too low (around the waist), he could be turned over by a wave because of the weight of his bag, and drown.

Folding spade.
© Mémorial de Caen.

A folding spade

The spade was as important as the rifle. It enabled soldiers to dig holes inside which they could crouch for protection. It was used throughout the entire Battle of Normandy. The GIs learned to dig silently, on their knees, to avoid alerting the enemy. The men could sometimes stay several days in these narrow holes, where they ate and rested, as they waited for the next assault.

On this picture, we can see both Allied and German material.
© Mémorial de Caen.

TM 30-602
RESTRICTED
FRENCH
PHRASE BOOK
SEPTEMBER 28, 1943
U. S. ARMY FIELD RATION K
DINNER UNIT
Packed By
American Chicle Company
Long Island City, New York
Supper
RATION TYPE K

Medical material

During the landings, the wounded were cared for direct on the beach but, later, throughout the Battle of Normandy, genuine hospitals were set up to the rear of the front. Surgeons operated on the seriously wounded in well-equipped operating theatres.

Floatation skirt.

The conversation guide

In his kit bag, each soldier was issued with a small vocabulary book to enable him to say a few words in French. For each word, he could read the translation and its pronunciation.
I am hungry: 'J'ai faim' (*jay fang*)
Bread: 'du pain' (*dew pang*)
I'm thirsty: 'J'ai soif' (*jay swaf*)
Water: 'de l'eau' (*duh lo*)
A cup of coffee: 'une tasse de café' (*ewn tass duh ka-fay*)

Conversation guide.

The K-ration

The K-ration was a soldier's daily food ration. It was packed inside a watertight cardboard box and was designed to fit inside a pocket. The ration included three full meals with canned meat (ham, chicken, pork, sausages) and cheese, powdered soup, biscuits and fruit paste, sachets of powdered milk, a packet of four cigarettes, chewing gum, three sugar lumps, powdered fruit juice, tablets to purify water, toilet paper, etc.

K-Ration.

D-DAY LANDING FIGURES

The Normandy Landings took long months of preparation. Figures show that it took huge quantities of material and tens of thousands of soldiers to successfully accomplish this exceptional military operation.

- **4 other landing** operations took place before Normandy. The landing operation on the Normandy beaches was not the first. In 1942, the Americans landed in North Africa (Morocco and Algeria), and in 1943, the British, Americans and Canadians set foot on the beaches of Sicily, then in Italy in 1944.
- **6 million tonnes** of material (guns, rifles, grenades, trucks, jeeps, tanks, cases of food, military tents, medical material, etc.) were produced in the United States and transported by ship to Great Britain.
- **3 million soldiers** formed the Allied armies. They came from **14 different countries**: Great Britain, the United States, Canada, France, New Zealand, Australia, Greece, Poland, Czechoslovakia, Belgium, Denmark, Luxembourg, Norway and the Netherlands.
- **1,500 British and American parachutists** jumped over Normandy on the night of the 5th to the 6th of June 1944. Their mission was to block the arrival of German reinforcements.
- **8,000 tonnes of bombs** were dropped on the night of the 5th to the 6th of June on the Atlantic Wall defences.
- **7,000 ships crossed** the English Channel on the night of the 5th to the 6th of June.
- **156,000 men** landed in Normandy.
- **10,300 of them were killed**, drowned, wounded or never found... (**6,000 Americans, 3,000 British and Canadians**, including **1,300 parachutists**). The forecast figure was: **2,500 unfit for combat** on the 6th of June.
- **20,000 vehicles** of all sorts were landed.
- **20,000 Norman civilians died** during the Battle of Normandy, from the 6th of June to the 21st of August 1944, essentially during the bombardment of towns.

LCA 1377

Soldiers in training in England.

Meeting between the generals to prepare for the Landings. We can see General Eisenhower in the centre.NARA.

THE D-DAY LANDING DATES

23rd March 1942: Hitler orders for the construction of the Atlantic Wall to prevent any possible landing. He has no idea of when and where.

19th August 1942: The Allies (the Canadians in particular) try to land in the port of Dieppe. Their mission fails. The Allies conclude that the landings will need to be on beaches, for ports are too well defended.

10th July 1943: The Allies land on beaches in Sicily. This landing will serve as a rehearsal for Normandy.

6th December 1943: The Allies agree to land in Normandy. They appoint General Eisenhower as commander-in-chief of the Allied armies.

5th June 1944: The parachutists and gliders transporting men and material take off for Normandy. They land by night.

6th June 1944: The American, British and Canadian troops land on the Normandy beaches.

7th June 1944: The few days that follow the landings are difficult for the Allies, who need to prevent the Germans from driving them back into the sea. The Battle of Normandy begins.

27th June 1944: The great port of Cherbourg is taken by the Allies.

15th August 1944: The Allies land in Provence (southern France).

21st August 1944: The Battle of Normandy is won by the Allies.

24th-25th August 1944: Paris is liberated.

TEST YOUR KNOWLEDGE...

TRUE OR FALSE?

1/ The Allies landed on beaches because powerful defences had been set up in ports.

2/ The Allied armies were commanded by the British General Montgomery.

3/ The codenames given to the landing beaches were: Utah Beach, Omaha Beach, George Beach, Coney Beach, Sword Beach.

4/ Omaha Beach is the one with the largest number of deaths. It is nicknamed 'Bloody Omaha'.

WHO IS HE?

1/ He is the American general who commanded the Allied armies that landed up to final victory in Germany. He later became President of the United States. Who is he?

2/ After the Desert War, Hitler sent him to France. He was in charge of speeding up work on the Atlantic Wall, which was not progressing quickly enough. Who is he?

3/ He is the British Prime Minister and is determined to fight to the bitter end against Hitler. Who is he?

QUIZ

1/ GI is the name given to: American soldiers / Canadian soldiers / British soldiers.

2/ To help them recognise each other, the American parachutists had: trumpets / crickets / bells.

3/ The date of 6th June 1944 is also known as: victory day / the shortest night / D-Day.

4/ The Normandy Landings were the first phase of the: Battle of Normandy / Battle of the Atlantic / Battle of Britain.

DING

Test answer

True or false?: 1/ True; 2/ False, they were commanded by General Eisenhower; 3/ False, they were named Utah Beach, Omaha Beach, Juno Beach, Gold Beach and Sword Beach; 4/ True.
Who is he?: 1/ General Dwight David Eisenhower; 2/ General Erwin Rommel; 3/ Winston Churchill.
Quiz: 1/ American soldiers; 2/ Crickets; 3/ D-Day; 4/ The Battle of Normandy.